Technique & Performance

ALL-IN-TWO

CW00669966

PIANO

Adventures® *by Nancy and Randall Faber*

THE BASIC PIANO METHOD

This book belongs to: _____

Note: All exercises and pieces are by
Nancy and Randall Faber unless otherwise noted.

Production: Jon Ophoff
Cover and Illustrations: Terpstra Design, San Francisco
Engraving: Dovetree Productions, Inc.

ISBN 978-1-61677-651-0

£6·25

Progress Chart

Keep track of your progress.
Colour or put a star sticker for each item.

		Technique & Performance	Lesson & Theory
	TECHNIQUE SECRETS	4-5	
☆	**1. Round Hand Shape (Hand Cups)**	4	8
☆	**2. Relaxed Wrist (Wrist Float-off)**	4	10
☆	**3. Light Hand Bounce (Woodpecker Taps)**	5	17
☆	**4. Finger Independence (Silent Play)**	5	32
	UNIT 1 Legato and Staccato		
☆	Canoe Ride/Kayak Ride *(No.1 Round Hand Shape)*	6	10
☆	Ferris Wheel Up/Down *(No.2 Relaxed Wrist)*	7	14-15
☆	Jumping Bean Race No.1 and No.2 *(No.3 Light Hand Bounce)*	8	17
☆	ETUDE: Mouse Hunt for Cheese	9	18
☆	Finger Games *(No.4 Finger Independence)*	10	20
☆	ETUDE: Legato Etude and Legato/Staccato Etude	11	20
☆	PERFORMANCE: The Wild Colt	12-13	21
	UNIT 2 Treble F-A-C-E		
☆	No Rain on My Spaceship *(No.1 Round Hand Shape)*	14	22
☆	ETUDE: Above the Pines	15	26
☆	PERFORMANCE: The Clock Shop	16-17	27
	UNIT 3 Treble C-D-E-F-G on the Stave		
☆	Paper Airplane Flight *(No.4 Finger Independence)*	18	32
☆	ETUDE: Two Songbirds	19	34
☆	PERFORMANCE: I'm a Fine Musician	20-21	34
	UNIT 4 Intervals (2nd, 3rd, 4th, 5th)		
☆	Horse Path *(No.3 Light Hand Bounce)*	22	39
☆	Mixed-Up Intervals *(No.1 Round Hand Shape)*	23	42-43
☆	ETUDE: A Merry March *(No.4 Finger Independence)*	24	47
☆	ETUDE: Pastel Painting *(No.2 Relaxed Wrist)*	25	48
☆	PERFORMANCE: Legend of the Buffalo	26-27	49

TECHNIQUE SECRETS

These four Technique Secrets are used as daily warm-ups for pieces and exercises in this book.
The "secrets" may be learned gradually and are highlighted in gold-coloured boxes throughout the pages.
For quick and easy use, the Lesson Book also refers to each correlating Technique Book page with this icon: ✍

The teacher should demonstrate each "technique secret" as it is introduced.

Four Technique Secrets

Technique means skill. These technique secrets will help you play pieces more easily.

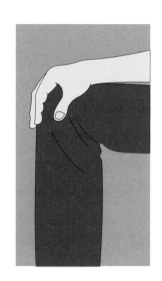

1. **The first secret is ROUND HAND SHAPE.**

Hand Cups

- Place your **right hand** over your kneecap.

- Keep that "hand shape" and s-l-o-w-l-y place your hand on the keyboard.

- Now do the same with your **left hand**.
  Try it hands together.

2. **The second secret is a RELAXED WRIST.**

Wrist Float-off (on the closed piano lid)

- Set your hands in a rounded hand position.

- Pretend a balloon on a string is slowly pulling your wrist upward. Let your wrist rise in s-l-o-w motion until only the **tip of finger 3** is touching the surface.*

- Now gently return to a normal playing position.

- **Do 2 "wrist float-offs" with right hand, then left hand.**
  Try it hands together.

*Teacher Note: The shoulder should not rise, but stay relaxed.

Teacher Note: The next secret teaches staccato, allowing the hand to bounce lightly from the wrist. The student should be coached to relax while tapping, so as not to stiffen the forearm.

3. **The third secret is a LIGHT HAND BOUNCE.**

Woodpecker Taps (on the closed piano lid)

- Place your **right hand** in a round hand shape.

- Perch your thumb on the *side tip* so your wrist doesn't sag.

- Lightly tap this rhythm with your fingertips
  (all fingers tap together).

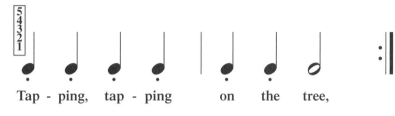

R.H.

Tap - ping,   tap - ping   on   the   tree,

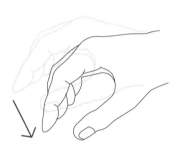

- Repeat *Woodpecker Taps* with your **left hand**.
  Now tap hands together.

4. **The fourth secret is FINGER INDEPENDENCE.**

Silent Play (on the closed piano lid)

- Silently play the **finger pattern** below.
  Remember to keep a round hand shape.

Say: **1 - 2 - 3 - 4 - 5 - 3 - 1**
└———— finger pattern ————┘

- Play **right hand (R.H.)**.

- Play **left hand (L.H.)**.

- Play **hands together (H.T.)**.

Lesson page 17 (Mexican Jumping Beans), page 32 (Paper Airplane)   5

Legato means a smooth and connected sound, with no break between tones.
When you play LEGATO, one finger goes down as the other finger comes up.

Technique Secret:
round hand shape (page 4)

Warm-up with *Hand Cups*.

Canoe Ride

Legato Steps for R.H.

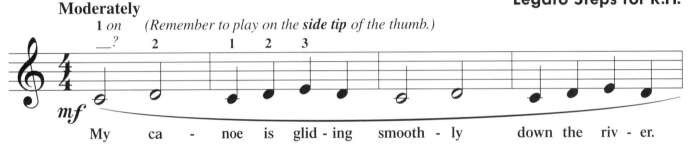

Moderately

1 *on* ___? (*Remember to play on the **side tip** of the thumb.*)

mf

My ca - noe is glid - ing smooth - ly down the riv - er.

I could go for - ev - er rid - ing on the riv - er, gen - tly glid - ing home.

Kayak Ride

Legato Steps for L.H.

Moderately

My kay - ak is glid - ing smooth - ly down the riv - er.

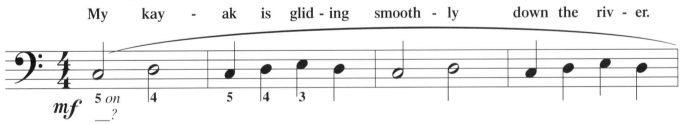

mf 5 *on* ___?

I could go for - ev - er rid - ing on the riv - er, gen - tly glid - ing home.

Lesson page 10 (Little River)

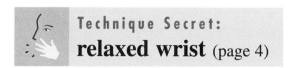
Warm-up with *Wrist Float-off.*

Play this **SKIPPING PATTERN** 3 times,
each time higher on the keyboard.

• Do a wrist float-off at the end of each line
to carry your hand *higher.*

Ferris Wheel Up
(for R.H. alone)

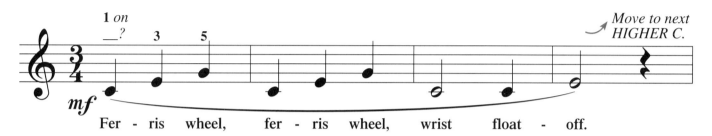

Fer - ris wheel, fer - ris wheel, wrist float - off.

Move to next HIGHER C.

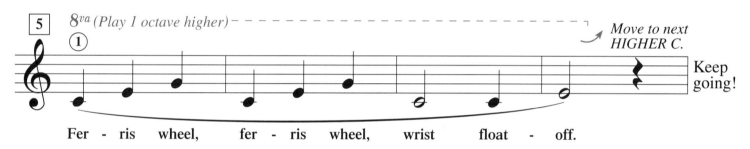

Fer - ris wheel, fer - ris wheel, wrist float - off.

Move to next HIGHER C.

Keep going!

Repeat the pattern again 1 octave higher.

Play this **SKIPPING PATTERN** 3 times,
each time lower on the keyboard.

• Do a wrist float-off at the end of each line
to carry your hand *lower.*

Ferris Wheel Down
(for L.H. alone)

Fer - ris wheel, fer - ris wheel, wrist float - off.

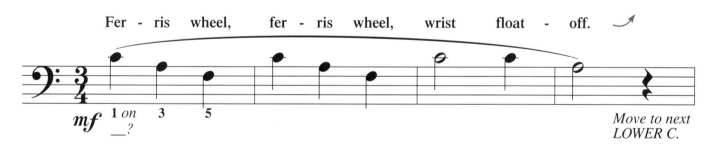

Move to next LOWER C.

Fer - ris wheel, fer - ris wheel, wrist float - off.

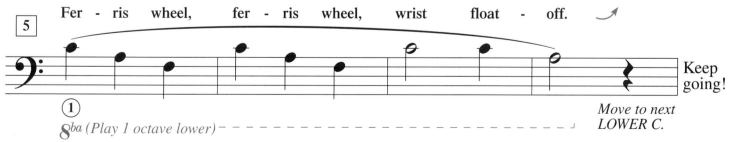

Keep going!

Move to next LOWER C.

Repeat the pattern again 1 octave lower.

Lesson pages 14-15 (Ferris Wheel)   7

Staccato means the notes are separated to create a crisp, bouncy sound.
To play staccato, lightly bounce from the wrist. Stay close to the keys!

Technique Secret:
light hand bounce (page 5)

Warm-up with *Woodpecker Taps*.

Jumping Bean Race No.1
(for R.H. alone)

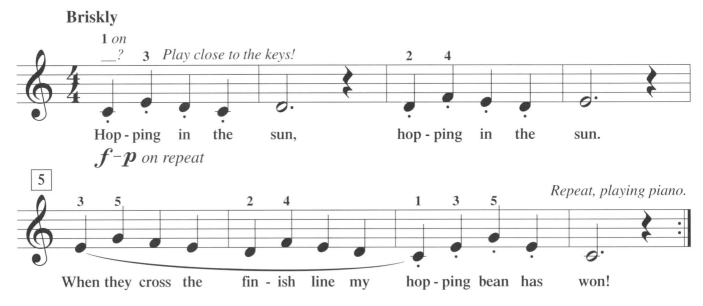

Briskly

1 *on*
__? 3 *Play close to the keys!* 2 4

Hop - ping in the sun, hop - ping in the sun.

f-p on repeat

5

3 5 2 4 1 3 5 *Repeat, playing piano.*

When they cross the fin - ish line my hop - ping bean has won!

Jumping Bean Race No.2
(for L.H. alone)

Briskly

Hop - ping in the sun, hop - ping in the sun.

1 *on* 3 2 4

__?

f-p on repeat

5 *Repeat, playing piano.*

When they cross the fin - ish line my hop - ping bean has won!

3 5 2 4 1 3 5

An **etude** (EH-tude) is a study piece.
• Say this word with your teacher.

In this etude, the L.H. **holds a note down**
while the R.H. plays *staccato*.

Mouse Hunt for Cheese

Sneaking quickly

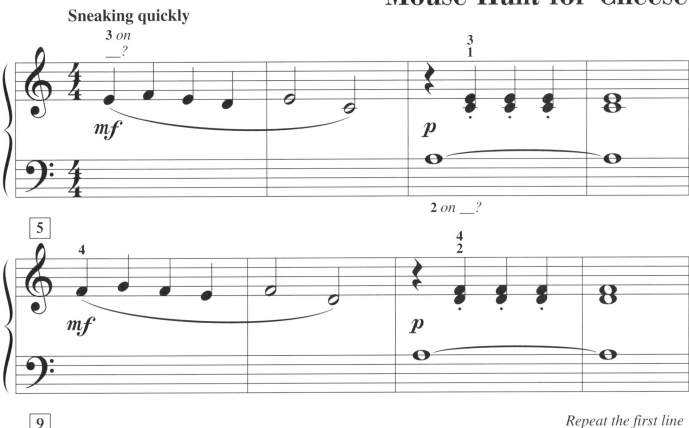

*Repeat the first line
to end the piece.*

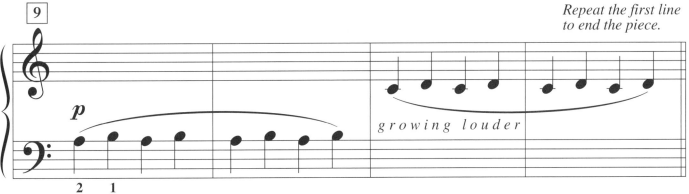

Teacher Duet: (Student plays *1 octave higher*)

Technique Secret:
finger independence (page 5)

Do *Silent Play* for R.H. with this pattern.

2 - 3 - 4 - 2 - 3 - 4 - 5 <u>hold</u>

- Play *f*, then *mf*, then *p*.

Finger Game No.1

R.H. C 5-Finger Scale

Louis Köhler
(1820-1886, Germany)
Op. 300

Steady   *Play 3 times.*

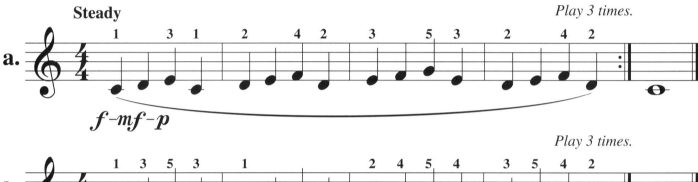

f-mf-p

Play 3 times.

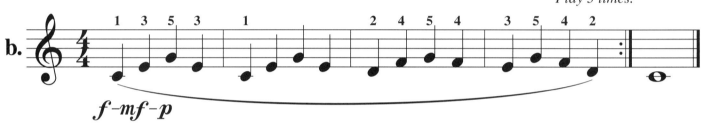

f-mf-p

Technique Secret:
finger independence (page 5)

Do *Silent Play* for L.H. with this pattern.

5 - 4 - 3 - 5 - 4 - 3 - 2 <u>hold</u>

Finger Game No.2

L.H. C 5-Finger Scale

Steady   *Play 3 times.*

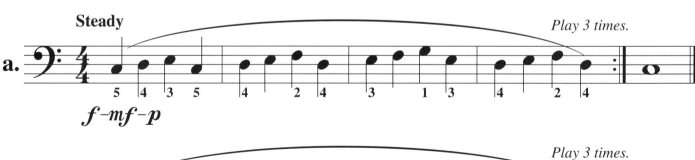

f-mf-p

Play 3 times.

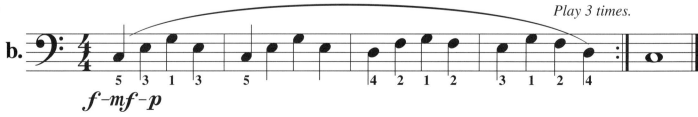

f-mf-p

Legato Etude

- Play hands separately. Watch for **steps** and **skips**.
- Play hands together. Listen for a smooth *legato*.

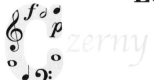

Carl Czerny
(1791-1857, Austria)
Op. 599

Legato/Staccato Etude

- Listen for a smooth *legato* and crisp *staccatos*.

Ferdinand Beyer
(1803-1863, Germany)
Op. 101

A good pianist plays the music with expression or feeling.

• Listen to your teacher play *The Wild Colt*. Does the music create a mood or **"sound picture"**?

• Can YOU create a "sound picture" as you practise *The Wild Colt*?

  1. Could the *staccato* sounds be horse hooves running quickly?
  2. For the *legato* section, can you picture the wild colt running up and down the hills?
  3. At the end of the piece, could the colt be disappearing into the moonlight?

The Wild Colt

N. Faber

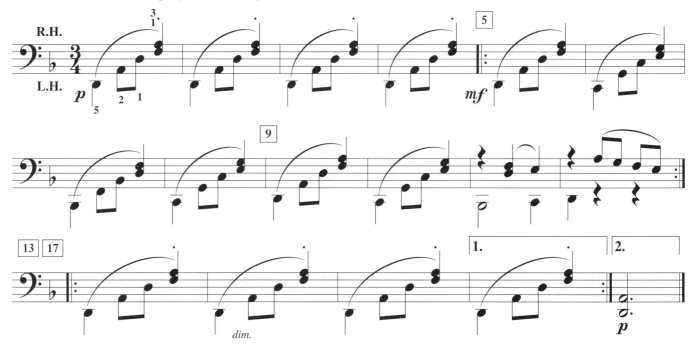

Lesson page 21 (Young Hunter)

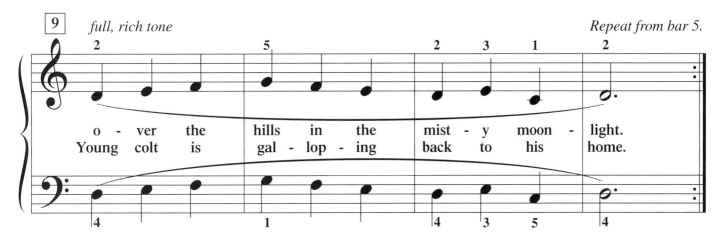

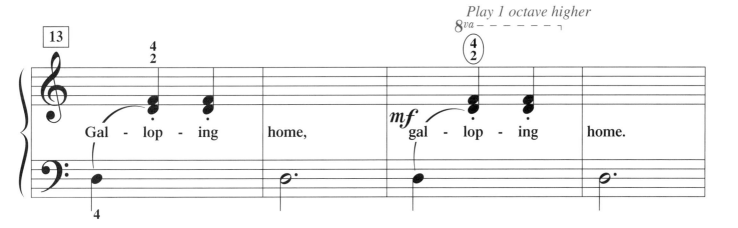

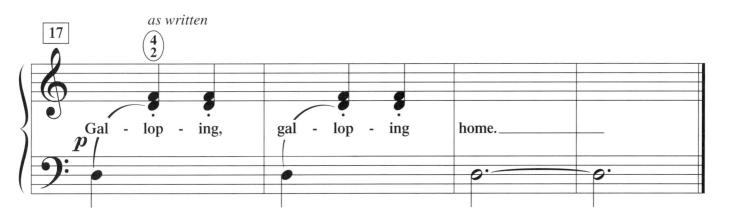

DISCOVERY Circle the **time signature**. What does it mean?

Technique Secret:
round hand shape (page 4)

Warm-up with *Hand Cups*.

- Imagine each note is a raindrop pinging on the metal spaceship.

- Use a crisp, *staccato* sound!

- Does this piece use **steps** or **skips**?

No Rain on My Spaceship

Bouncing happily

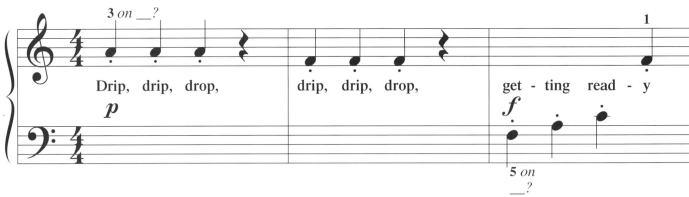

Drip, drip, drop,   drip, drip, drop,   get - ting read - y

p   *f*

3 *on ___?*   5 *on ___?*   1

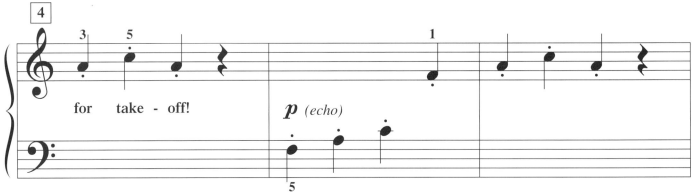

for take - off!   *p (echo)*

4   3   5   1   5

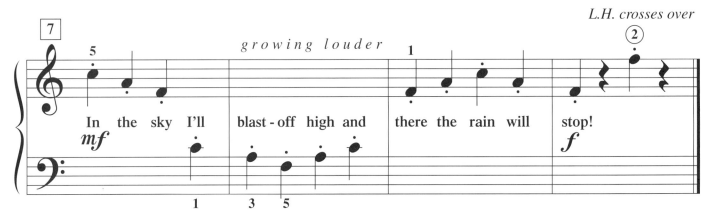

In the sky I'll   blast - off high and   there the rain will   stop!

mf   *growing louder*   *f*

7   5   1   *L.H. crosses over* ②

1   3   5

This etude will help you practise **wrist float-offs** with the beautiful sound of the pedal.

- Brace **R.H. finger 3** for a round hand shape.

- Imagine your right hand as the wing of an eagle, soaring high on the "air currents."

Above the Pines

Hold the sustain pedal down throughout.

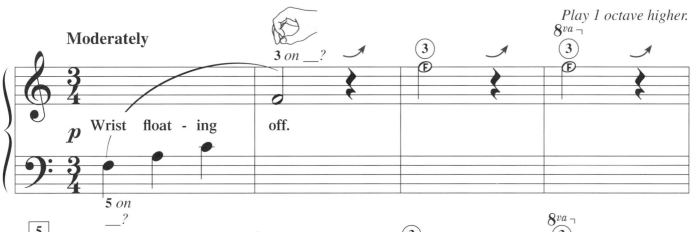

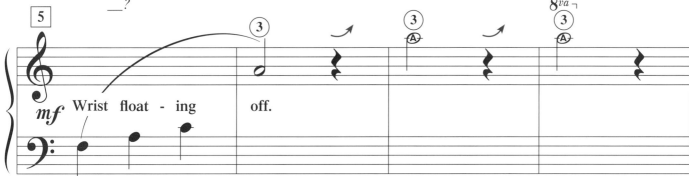

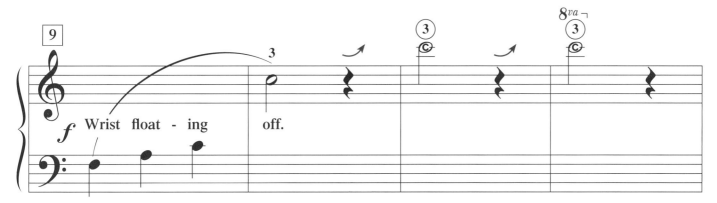

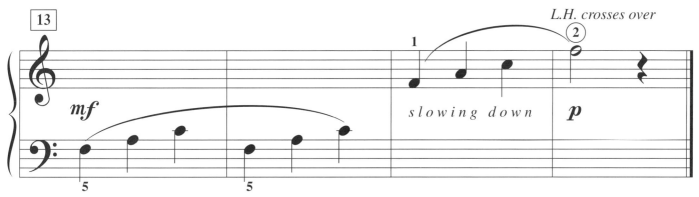

DISCOVERY Can you play this etude a step *higher* (beginning on G)?

• Can you keep the clock shop ticking in perfect time?

The Clock Shop

Moderately

Come to the clock shop; you'll hear the tick-tock all day long!

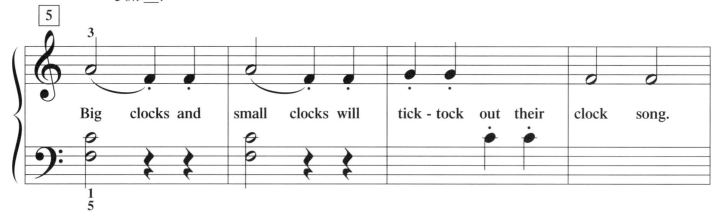

Big clocks and small clocks will tick-tock out their clock song.

Teacher Duet: (Student plays *1 octave higher*)

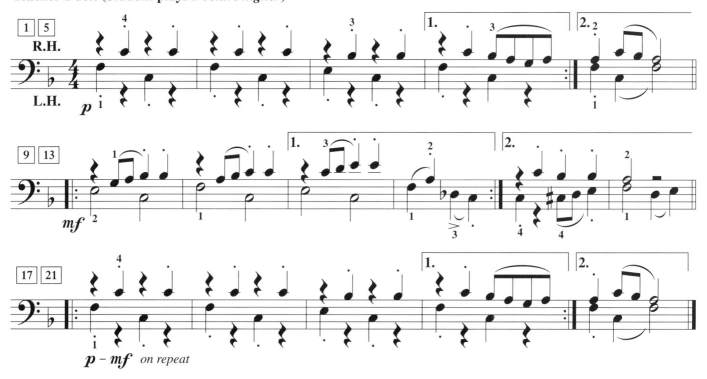

Lesson page 27 (Li'l Liza Jane)

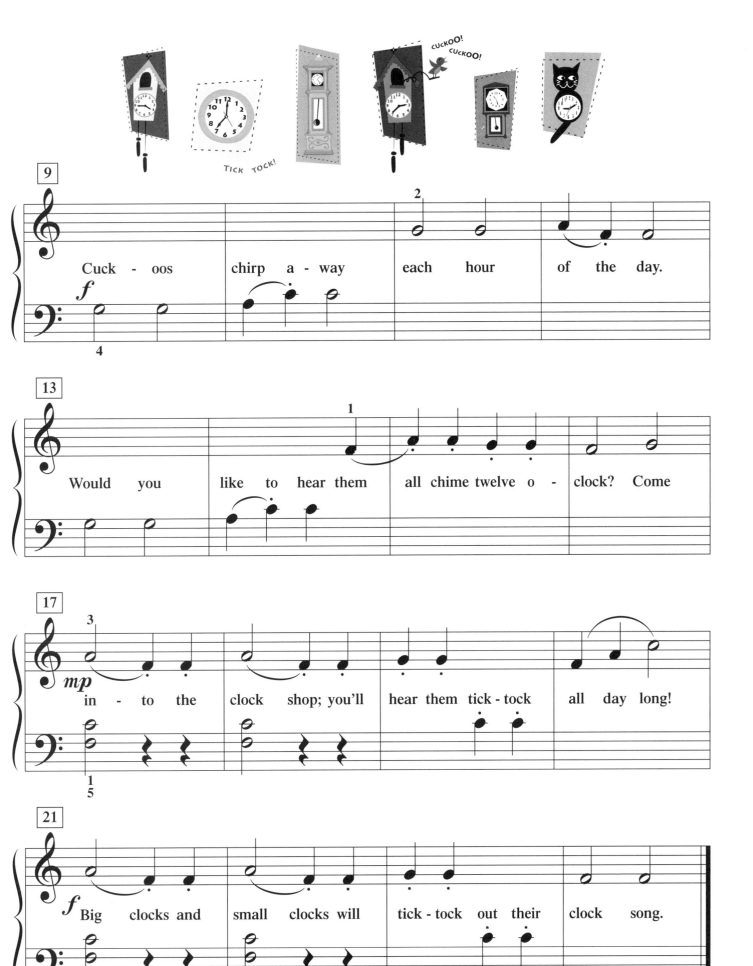

9

Cuck - oos | chirp a - way | each hour | of the day.

f

4

13

Would you | like to hear them | all chime twelve o - clock? Come

1

17

mp

in - to the | clock shop; you'll | hear them tick - tock | all day long!

3

1
5

21

f Big clocks and | small clocks will | tick - tock out their | clock song.

DISCOVERY Where do *bars 1–8* return later in the piece? Show your teacher.

17

Do *Silent Play* hands alone, then hands together.

pattern: **1** - **3** - **2** - **4** - **3** ^{hold} **5** ^{hold}

Paper Airplane Flight

A pianist with good technique **PREPARES** the next hand position.

• Move one hand to the next position while the other hand is still playing.

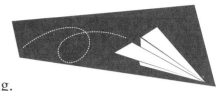

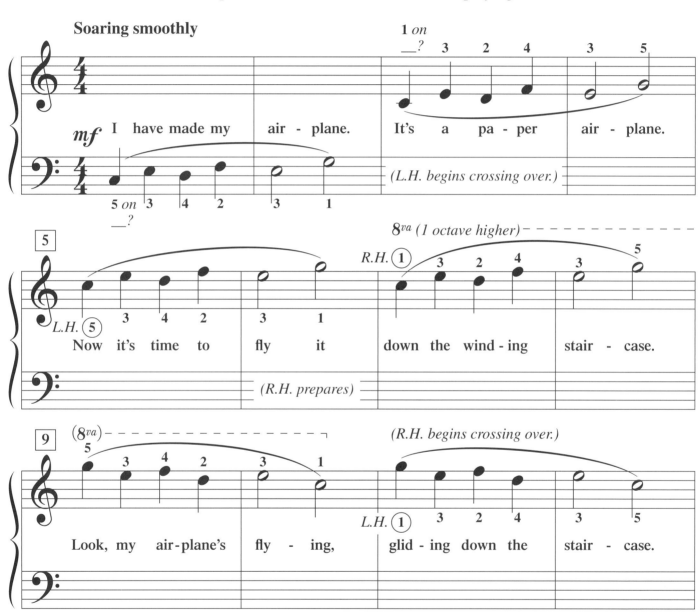

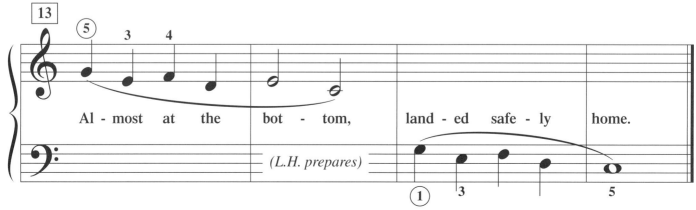

Lesson page 32 (Paper Airplane)

In this etude, both hands are equal partners. Imagine two birds singing together.

- First play **hands separately**.

- Then play **hands together**. Notice both hands move up and down at the *same* time.

Two Songbirds

Ferdinand Beyer
(1803-1863, Germany)
Op. 101

I'm a Fine Musician

Bright and snappy

Traditional
adapted

growing louder

p Oom-pah, oom-pah, | oom-pah-pah. | Oom-pah, oom-pah, | oom-pah-pah.

Play the L.H. one octave LOWER throughout.

5

f I'm a fine mu - si - cian, I | prac - tise ev - 'ry | day. Oh!

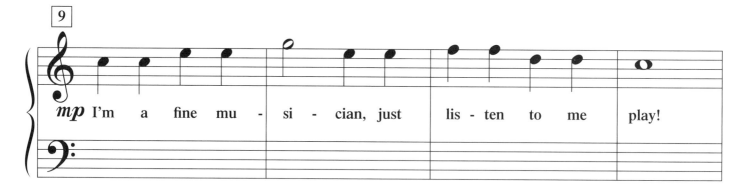

9

mp I'm a fine mu - si - cian, just | lis - ten to me | play!

13

f Tu - ba, | tu - ba, | Hear me play my | tu - ba.

Repeat and fade as the
musicians march away!

DISCOVERY Play this piece with the R.H. 1 octave HIGHER than written throughout the piece.
Now the flute will sound like a piccolo!

Technique Secret:
light hand bounce (page 5)

- Write your own rhythm in $\frac{4}{4}$ using staccatos.

- Do *Woodpecker Taps* using your rhythm.

$\frac{4}{4}$

Horse Path
(for R.H. alone)

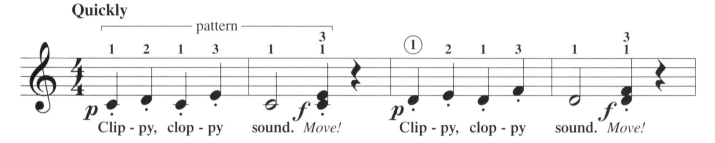

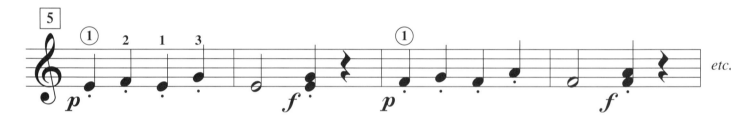

Continue this pattern beginning on G, A, B, and C.

Horse Path
(for L.H. alone)

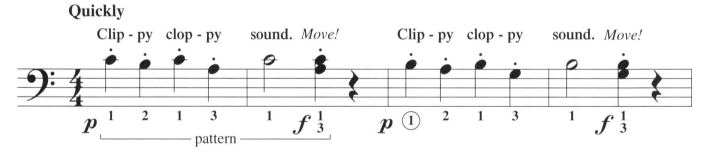

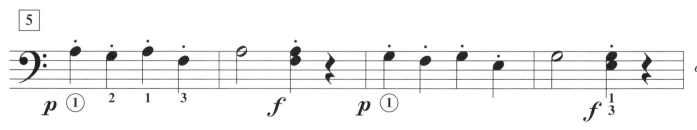

Continue this pattern beginning on F, E, D, and C.

**Technique Secret:
round hand shape** (page 4)

Warm-up with *Hand Cups*.

Mixed-Up Intervals
(for R.H. alone)

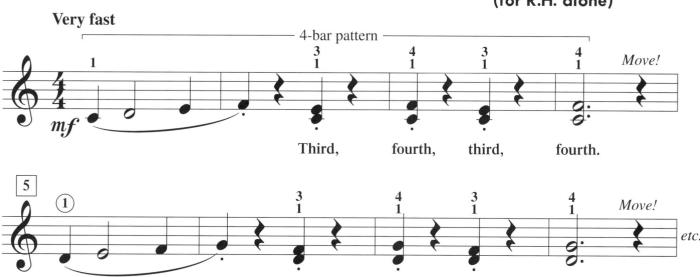

Continue this pattern beginning on E, F, G, A, B, and C.

• Here is a similar pattern
for the left-hand.

Mixed-Up Intervals
(for L.H. alone)

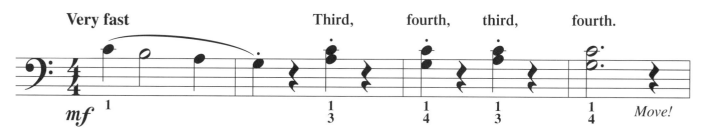

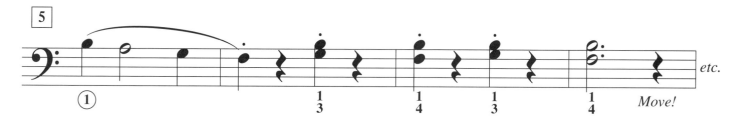

Continue this pattern beginning on A, G, F, E, D, and C.

Technique Secret:
finger independence (page 5)

Do *Silent Play* separate hands, then hands together.

1 - 3 - 2 - 5 - 3 <u>hold</u>

Notice the L.H. has a pattern of **two notes**—C and B.

• Circle where the pattern changes to a new note—G.

A Merry March

Cornelius Gurlitt
(1820–1901, Germany)
Op. 117, No. 1, adapted

Happily

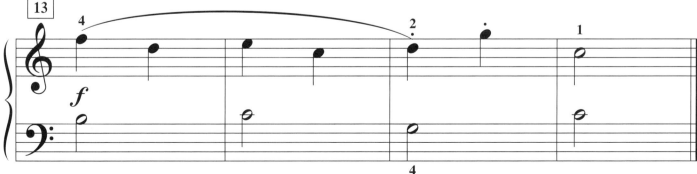

Lesson page 47 *(Runaway Rabbit)*

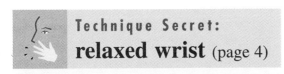

Technique Secret:
relaxed wrist (page 4)

Warm-up with *Wrist Float-off*.

Pastel Painting

Hold the right foot pedal down throughout.

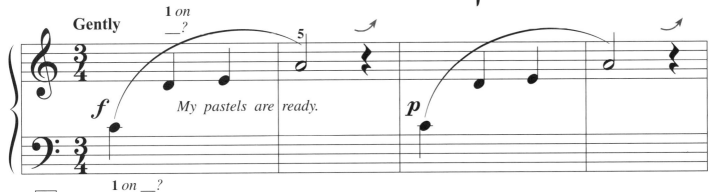

My pastels are ready.

I start to paint …   *… purples and pinks.*

The colours mingle with soft blues.

When I'm done I'll set it by the window.

Teacher Duet: (Student plays *1 octave higher*)

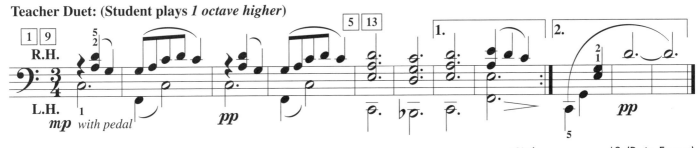

Lesson page 48 (Rain Forest)

Different **DYNAMICS** (*p, mp, mf, f*) help to make a piece interesting.

In this piece, **you can choose the dynamics**.

- First, read the words and play the music.

- Then write dynamic marks in the boxes given.

- Now play the piece and enjoy your version of *Legend of the Buffalo*!

Legend of the Buffalo

With spirit

N. Faber

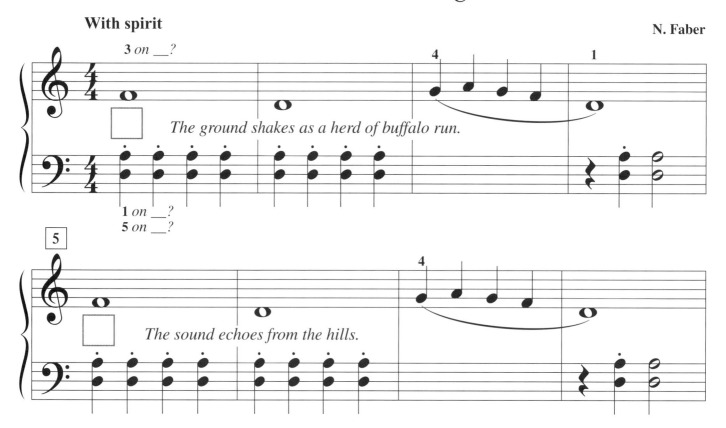

The ground shakes as a herd of buffalo run.

3 *on* __?

1 *on* __?
5 *on* __?

The sound echoes from the hills.

Teacher Duet: (Student plays *as written*)

Note: Follow the dynamic marks chosen by the student.

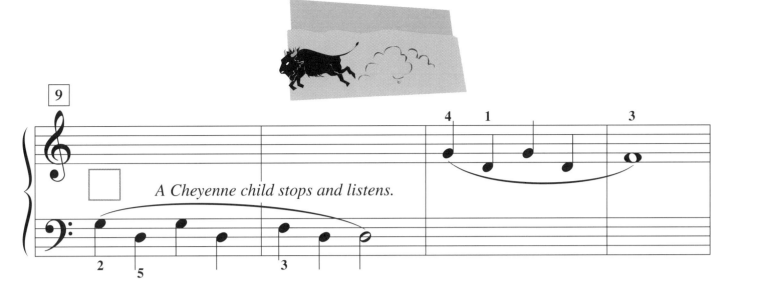

A Cheyenne child stops and listens.

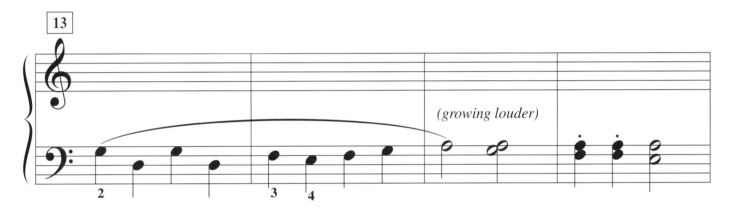

(growing louder)

A dust cloud rises as the buffalo thunder by.

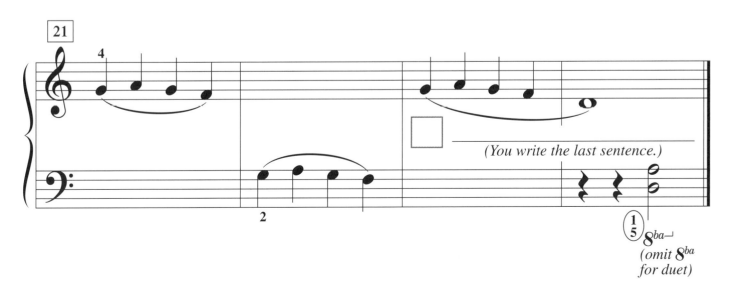

(You write the last sentence.)

(omit 8ᵇᵃ for duet)

27

Technique Secret:
finger independence (page 5)

Do *Silent Play* separate hands, then hands together.

3 - 5 - 4 - 3 - 5 - 4 - 3 <u>hold</u>

- First play on the **closed piano lid**.
  Hint: Both hands use the *same fingering*.

Playing by the Stream
C 5-Finger Scale

"Program" each musical pattern into your hands so you can even play it in the dark!

- First, memorise the pattern and play watching your hands.

- Then play it looking **straight ahead**, NOT at your hands. Do you have the pattern on "automatic?"

Robot in the Dark

(for R.H. alone)

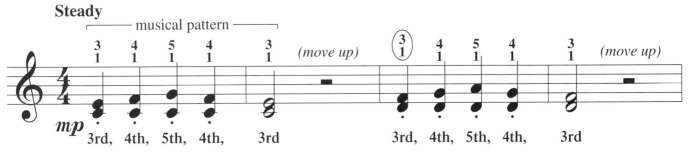

3rd, 4th, 5th, 4th, 3rd   3rd, 4th, 5th, 4th, 3rd

Continue this pattern beginning on G, A, B, and C.

Robot in the Dark

(for L.H. alone)

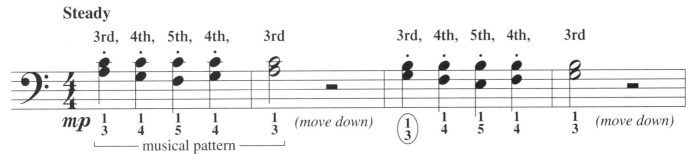

Continue this pattern beginning on F, E, D, and C.

Lesson page 54 (No Moon Tonight)   29

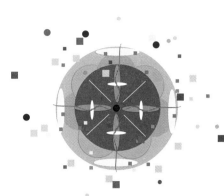

Have you ever looked through a kaleidoscope?
You would see many beautiful colours.

In music, playing the **dynamics** creates "musical colours."

- Create "musical colours" by following the dynamics closely.

- Before playing, name the **intervals** (2nd, 3rd, 4th, or 5th).

Hold the sustain pedal down throughout.

Kaleidoscope Colours

N. Faber

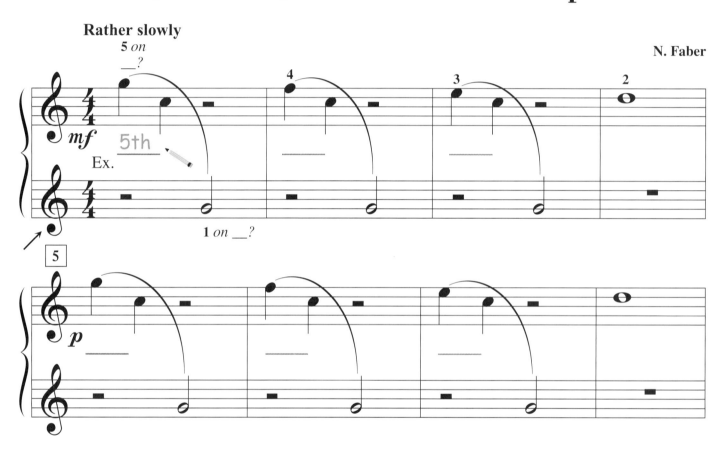

Teacher Duet: (Student plays *as written*) Teacher pedals for duet.

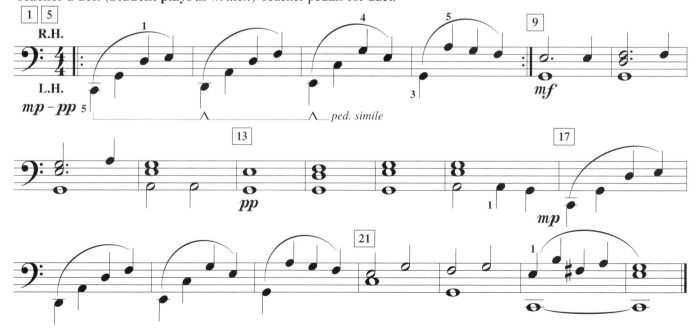

30   Lesson page 56 (Grumpy Old Troll)

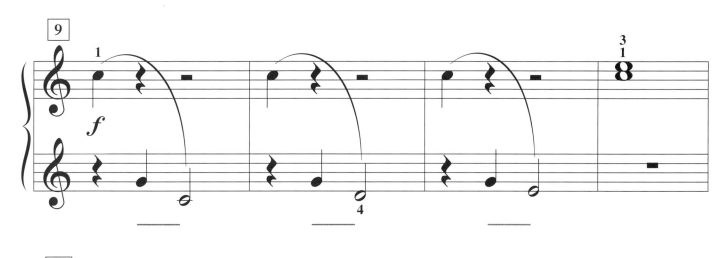

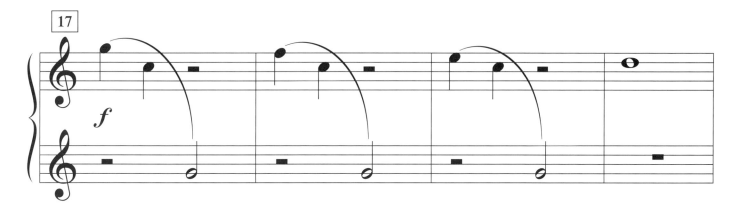

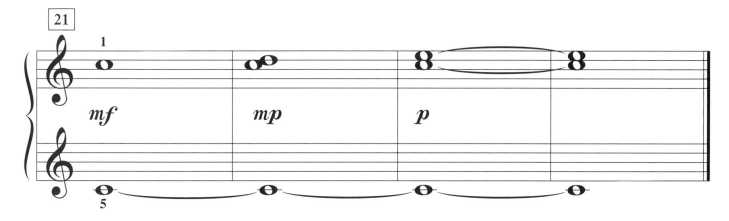

Use your imagination and choose a colour for each dynamic mark.

p _____ *mp* _____ *mf* _____ *f* _____

Technique Secret:
relaxed wrist (page 4)

Warm-up with *Wrist Float-off.*

- When playing from a **white key** to a **black key**,
  let your hand roll forward (toward the piano).

- As your fingers "walk up" to the black key,
  your wrist will rise *slightly*.

Play
L.H.
walk up

Play
R.H.
walk up

Magic Sparkles

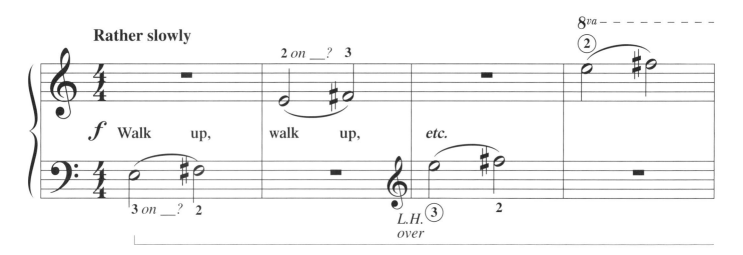

Rather slowly

2 on __? 3

f Walk up, walk up, *etc.*

3 on __? 2

L.H. ③ over

8*va* - - - - - - - - - - -
②

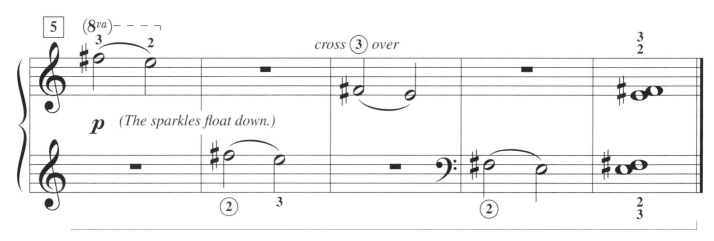

5 (8*va*)- - - -

p (The sparkles float down.)

cross ③ over

 **CHALLENGE SECTION**
You and your teacher may explore new **5-finger scales** that use *sharps (and flats)* on page 54.

This etude uses **half steps** (semitones) played quickly on the keyboard. How quickly can your clown move?

Crazy Clown

Music by N. Faber
Words by Crystal Bowman

Quickly, with mischief

(prepare L.H.)

Come and see the cra - zy clown when the cir - cus comes to town.

1 on __?

move up!

He's so fun - ny, he's so sil - ly, he at - tracts the big - gest crowd.

grow louder

He can jug - gle bright red balls, when he does he al - ways falls.

He's so fun - ny, he's so sil - ly, makes me laugh out loud! *Ha!*

L.H. gets ready

LOWEST C!

DISCOVERY In which line of music does the R.H. play only **half steps** (semitones)? Line _____

Lesson page 60 (Russian Sailor Dance)   33

Two Little Marches

A Sunny Parade

Daniel Gottlob Türk
(1750-1813, Germany)
original form

DISCOVERY

Name the interval as a **2nd**, **3rd**, **4th**, or **5th** in the blanks for this piece.

Teacher Duet: (Student plays *1 octave higher*)

(duet by authors)

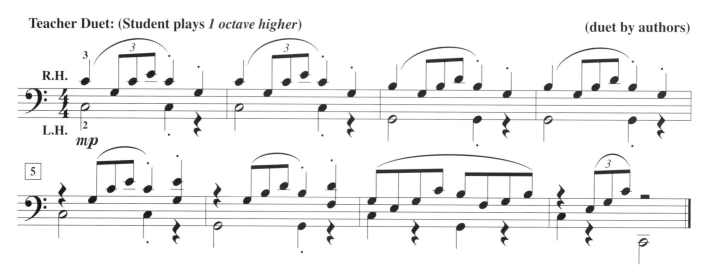

- Notice how the flat makes it sound like a rainy day!

A Rainy Parade

Rather slowly

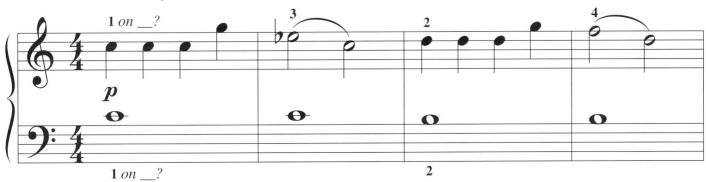

DISCOVERY Create a longer piece with a happy ending. Play *A Sunny Parade*, *A Rainy Parade*, then *A Sunny Parade* for the sun to come out again.

Teacher Duet: (Student plays *1 octave higher*)

**Technique Secret:
round hand shape** (page 4)

Warm-up with *Hand Cups*.

This piece uses only **tonic** and **dominant** notes.

- Hint: Begin crossing the *left hand over* while the right hand is still playing.

Jumps and Slides

📖 Lesson page 64 (Two-Note March)

This piece combines many of the musical ideas you have learned:

1. steady rhythm
2. legato and staccato
3. dynamics
4. listening

• Does your performance include them all?

Journey by Camel

Music by N. Faber
Words by Crystal Bowman

DISCOVERY

Can you play the right hand one octave *higher*?

Technique Secret:
round hand shape (page 4)

C Chord Warm-up

Warm-up with *Hand Cups*.

- For *forte* chords, play to the bottom of the keys with a relaxed wrist.

- For *piano* chords, play lightly and close to the keys.

C Chord Study

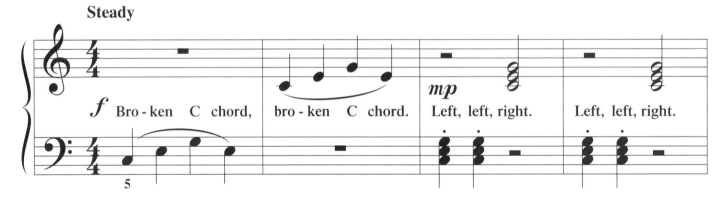

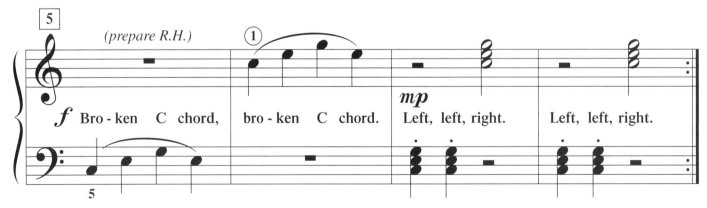

Teacher Duet: (Student plays *1 octave higher*)

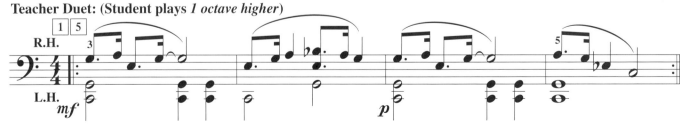

Lesson page 68 (The C Chord)

This etude helps you practise an *expressive* ending.

For the last line of this piece:

- Practise s-l-o-w-i-n-g down and getting softer.
- Do a wrist float-off on the last note.
- Lift the pedal and place both hands in your lap.

Hold the sustain pedal down throughout.

Carousel

Flowing smoothly

N. Faber

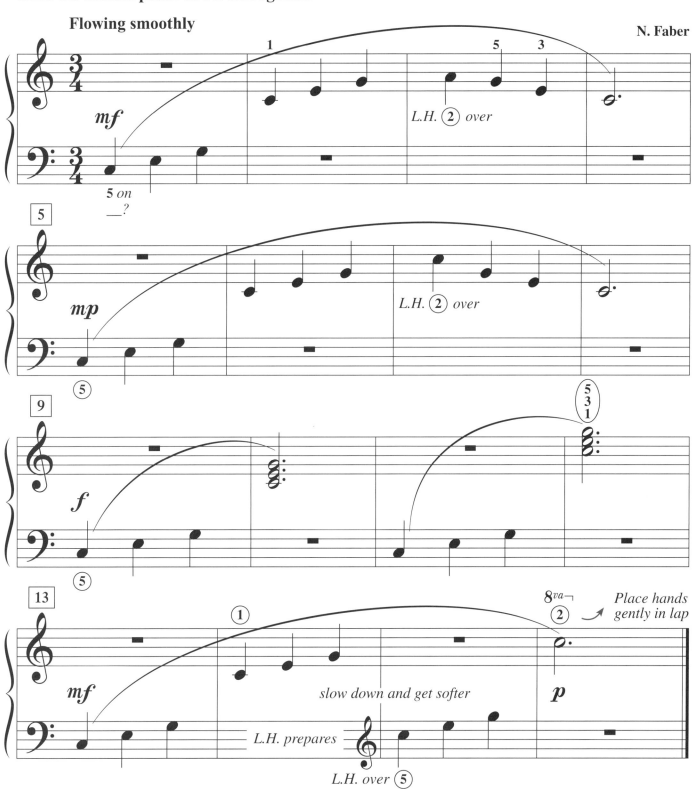

- Did you play an expressive ending?

- Circle the **dynamic marks** before you begin. Hint: There are 5.

Hill and Gully Rider

Fast and fun

Jamaican Folk Song

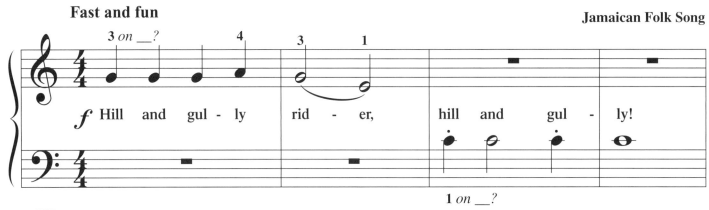

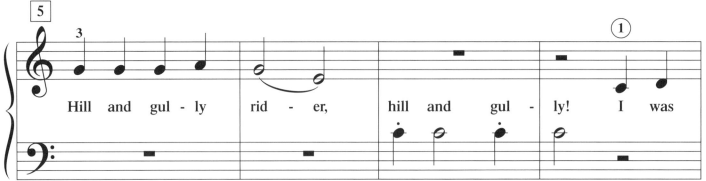

Teacher Duet: (Student plays *1 octave higher*)

Lesson page 72 (My Pony)

Do *Woodpecker Taps* using this rhythm:

Little Star Chords

C 5-Finger Scale

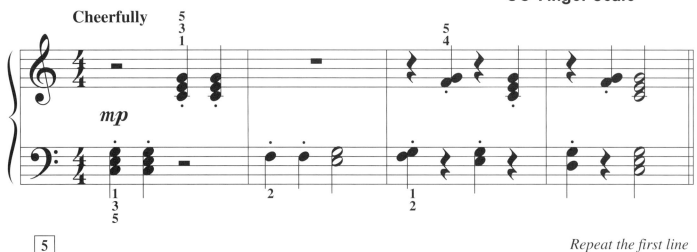

Repeat the first line to end the song.

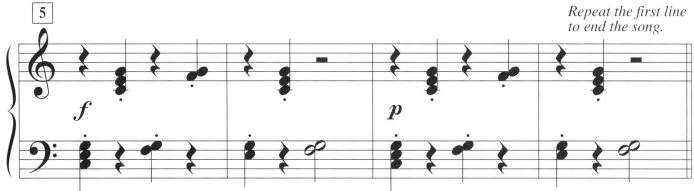

Teacher Duet: (Student plays *as written*)

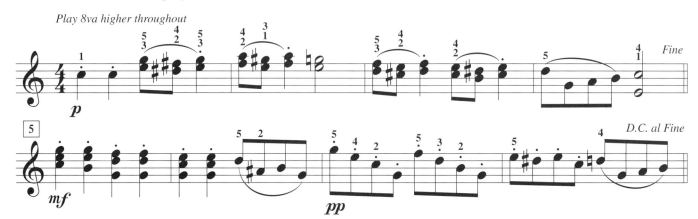

Melody: the tune

Harmony: notes or chords played with the melody

This etude helps you practise making the harmony
softer than the melody.

The Frog Prince

Happily

- Which hand has the melody?

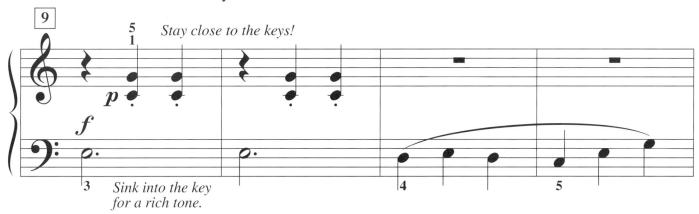

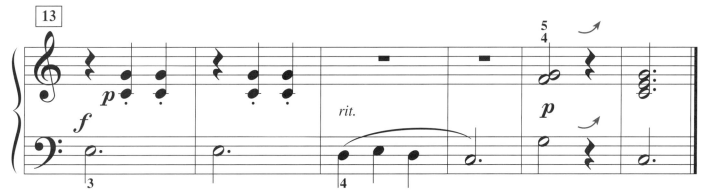

Lesson page 74 ("London" Symphony Theme)   43

This is a L.H. study for steady crotchets.
- Remember to play on **firm fingertips**.
- Play it low on the keyboard.

Walking Bass Etude

Louis Köhler
(1820-1886, Germany)
Op. 300

Strong and steady

8ba or 15ba (two octaves) LOWER throughout

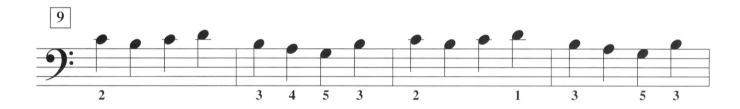

Teacher Duet for pages 44-45: (Student plays *1 or 2 octaves lower*)

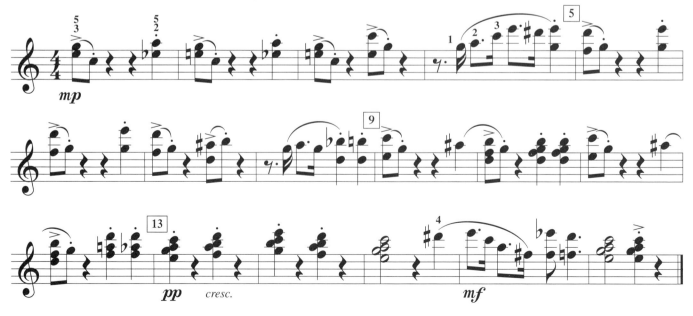

Lesson pages 76-77 (Shepherd's Song)

- Now play **I** and **V7** chords with this L.H. etude.
  Are you still playing on firm fingertips?

Walking Bass Etude
with Chords!

Strong and steady

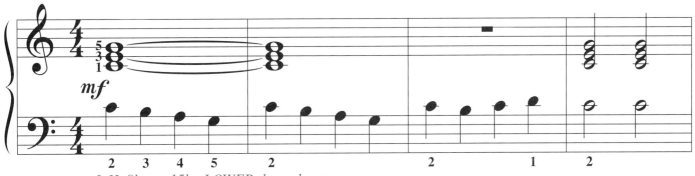

L.H. 8ba or 15ba LOWER throughout

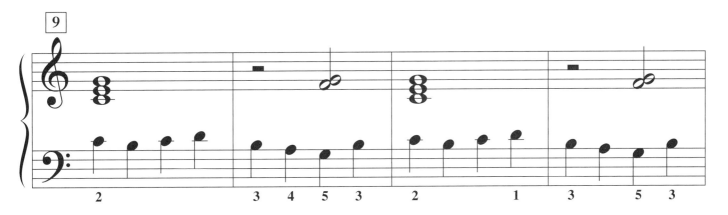

I've Got Music

Moderate beat

I tell my hon - ey
I love to sing it,

I don't have mon - ey,
to sway and swing it.

but I've got mu - sic down in my soul.
Yes, I've got mu - sic down in my soul.

Teacher Duet: (Student plays *1 octave higher*)

Lesson page 76-77 (Shepherd's Song)

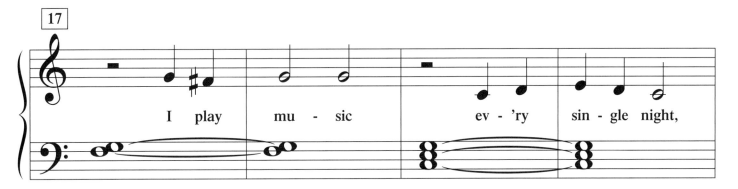

I play mu - sic ev - 'ry sin - gle night,

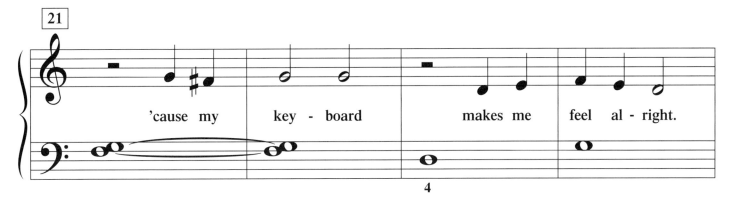

'cause my key - board makes me feel al - right.

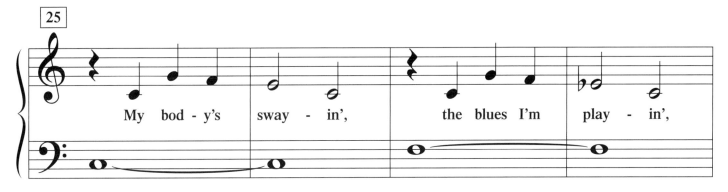

My bod - y's sway - in', the blues I'm play - in',

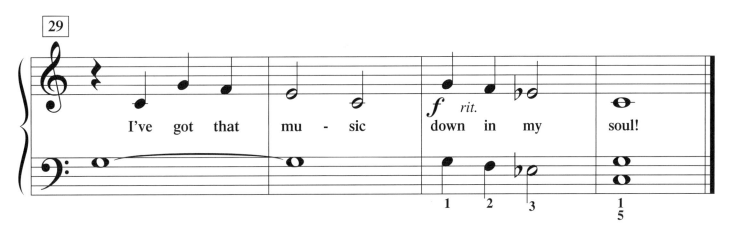

I've got that mu - sic down in my soul!

DISCOVERY

Label each **V7** chord in this piece.

Technique Secret:
finger independence (page 5)

Do *Silent Play* separate hands, then hands together.

5 - 4 - 3 - 4 - 5 <u>hold</u>

This exercise uses 4 different **G 5-finger scales**.

• Before playing, find and circle the *ritard*.

Backstage Warm-up

Moderately

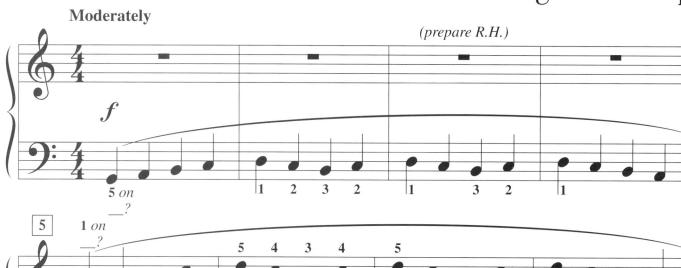

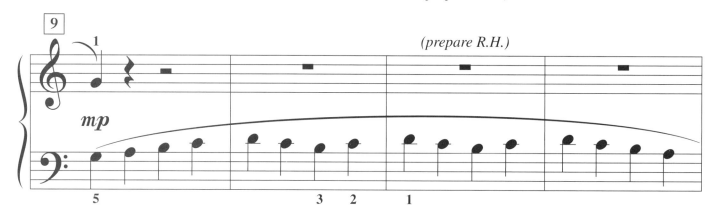

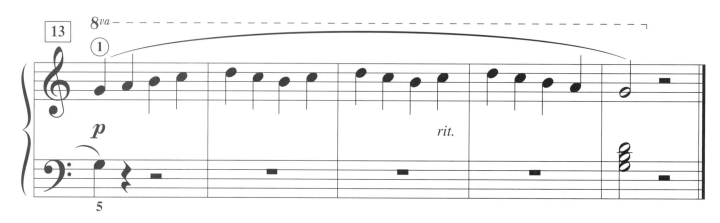

Upbeat Rule: Play the *upbeat* lightly,
then play a stronger tone on the *downbeat*.
Note: An upbeat is also known as an anacrusis.

This etude is a staccato piece with **accents**.

- Play with a steady beat and rhythmic accents!
  Remember the *ritard* at the end.

Tick-Tock Etude

G 5-Finger Scale

Happily

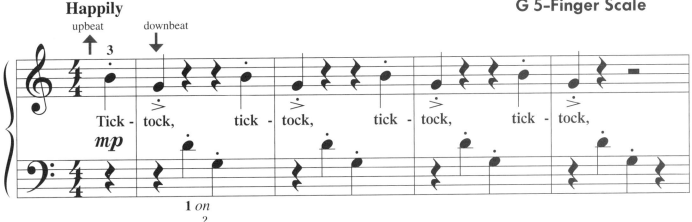

Tick - tock,   tick - tock,   tick - tock,   tick - tock,

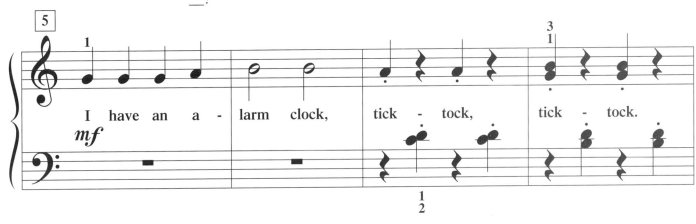

I have an a - larm clock,   tick - tock,   tick - tock.

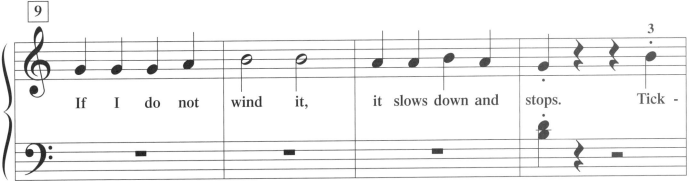

If I do not   wind it,   it slows down and   stops.   Tick -

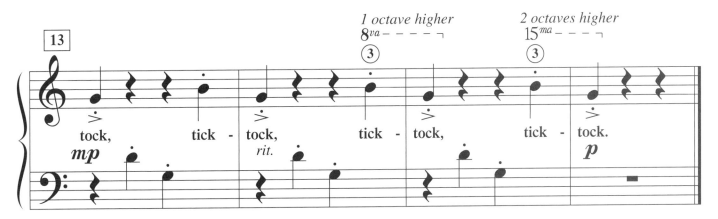

tock,   tick - tock,   tick - tock,   tick - tock.

📖 Lesson page 84 (The Dreydl Song)   49

Pop! Goes the Weasel is a jig that dates back over 200 years to England. The tune is also known from jack-in-the-box toys. When the tune gets to "POP," the "jack" pops up.

- Can you sing this song with your teacher before you play it?

Pop! Goes the Weasel

_____ 5-Finger Scale

Very fast

17th Century English Song

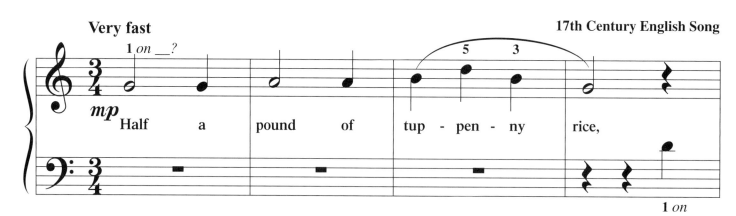

Half a pound of tup - pen - ny rice,

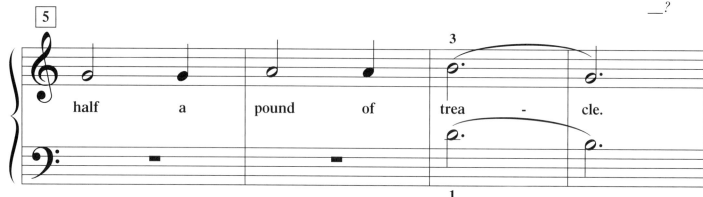

half a pound of trea - cle.

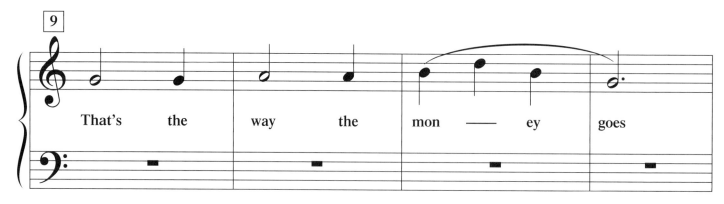

That's the way the mon — ey goes

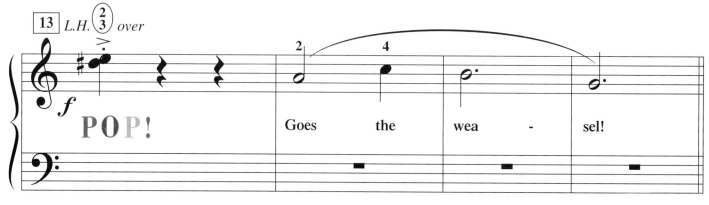

POP! Goes the wea - sel!

50   Lesson page 85 (Jumbo's Lullaby)

The San Francisco Trolley

_____ 5-Finger Scale

Teacher Note: D and A 5-Finger Scales are introduced with notation at Level 2A.
Students will benefit from learning these keyboard patterns away from the stave at Level 1.

I can have a biscuit when I get to the top!

For Adventurers

Explore some or all of these scales with your teacher.

• Use the **Adventure Warm-Up** on p. 55 for each scale.

• Transpose pieces from the book to these adventurous keys.

Think: Vanilla Biscuit with Chocolate in the Middle

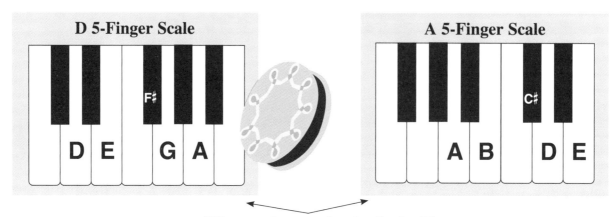

D 5-Finger Scale

F#

D E G A

A 5-Finger Scale

C#

A B D E

Why are these scales the "twins"?

Yum! Double Chocolate

E 5-Finger Scale

F# G#

E A B

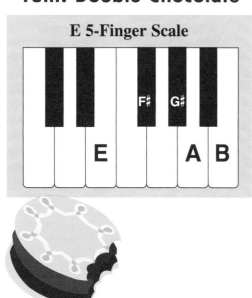

Who Moved the Chocolate?

F 5-Finger Scale

B♭

F G A C

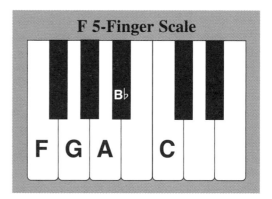

Adventure Warm-up in C

YOU CAN DO IT!

Moderately

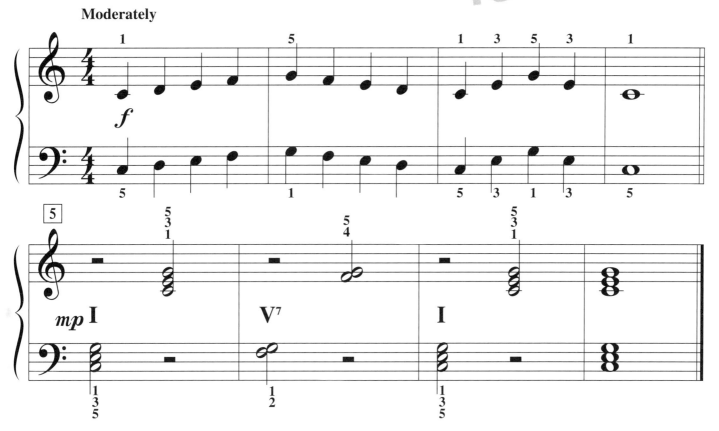

Adventure Warm-up in G

WAY TO GO!

Moderately

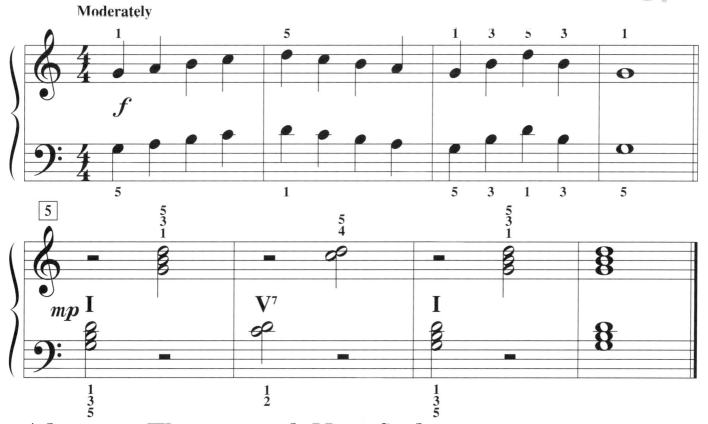

Adventure Warm-up with More Scales

Play the Adventure Warm-Up using the scales you have learned:

 C   D   E   F   G   A

Certificate of Fabulous Fingers

Congratulations to:

_____

(Your Name)

You have completed LEVEL 1 TECHNIQUE & PERFORMANCE

and are now ready for LEVEL 2A

**LESSON
& THEORY**

**TECHNIQUE
& PERFORMANCE**

Teacher:_____

Date:_____